# THE MYSTERY of the GRAND CANYON and CLIMATE CHANGE

By Randy Persson

Illustrations by Thomas Rodriguez

**INKWELL BOOKS**
Writing-Publishing-Printing

ISBN: 978-1-7366445-7-7
Library of Congress Control Number: 2020982625

Published by Inkwell Books LLC
10632 North Scottsdale Road, Unit 695
Scottsdale, AZ 85254
Tel. 480-315-3781
E-mail info@inkwellbooksllc.com
Website www.inkwellbooksllc.com

**INKWELL™ BOOKS**
Writing-Publishing-Printing

*I dedicate this book to my wife Rose.*

*Your love gave me the strength*

*to climb out of the Canyon when*

*I thought I couldn't take another step.*

*And to all the children with asthma at*

*Camp Not-A-Wheeze, I dedicate*

*the sales proceeds from book sales.*

*May we all treasure the breath of life.*

# Forward By My Dad

Little did we know when we planned to hike the Grand Canyon that the awe and magnificence of its creation and evolution would not only test us physically but also teach us how climate change created this beautiful Canyon.

We sought to discover how the Grand Canyon was formed and we were not disappointed. Our focus was on the beauty and depth of the Canyon, on its vastness, on the geology and the stories it told.

What we discovered was more than beauty, rocks and a mighty river that continues to carve the Canyon to this day. We saw the earth open up before our eyes and challenge us to understand our evolving planet.

We are neither geologists, historians nor meteorologists. We are simply people who walk on planet Earth and who can witness her mysteries should we take the time.

These discoveries were a true revelation to be able to see up close and personal how millions of years of changing climate patterns, earthquakes and volcanos along with a raging River to this day serve to carve and etch this beautiful Canyon.

(Thank you to Wayne Ranney for his insightful and compelling book, "Carving Grand Canyon")

And a special thank you to Marjorie Rice for her thoughtful and creative editing.

# Table of Contents

Forward By My Dad                                                    i

Table of Contents                                                    iii

Chapter 1    Dawn at the Edge                                        1

Chapter 2    First Steps                                             5

Chapter 3    Kaibab Formation                                        11

Chapter 4    Ancient Ones                                            15

Chapter 5    Mules                                                   19

Chapter 6    Colorado River and Phantom Ranch                        23

Chapter 7    Indian Garden                                           27

Chapter 8    The Rim                                                 31

Reflections                                                          35

# CHAPTER 1
# Dawn at the Edge

The first thing you need to know about hiking the Grand Canyon is you start early – way before the sun comes up. That's what my Dad said anyway, when he shook my brother and me awake on the first morning of our hike.

We got dressed, had some breakfast and then set off. Funny, even though I couldn't see it, I could feel it – like some huge, dark, cold being just out of reach.

The sky got lighter and as we approached the edge, the sun came up over the rim, pouring light on the Canyon and stopping us in our tracks.

For a few seconds we just stared, holding our breath and watching the shadows change.

"Awesome," Dad whispered.

"Wow, are we going in there?" my little brother Drew said.

I felt like one of those intrepid explorers we read about in history class, setting out on an adventure to a place no one had ever seen before us. Of course, we weren't the first, but it was a first time for us, and I couldn't wait to get started

I'm Taylor, and my Dad and brother and I were on this hike with Rick, my Dad's business partner, and his son Ryan. Ryan and I are the same age, and we were as nervous as Drew but didn't want to show it.

We had met at the Maswik Lodge the night before to map out our hike. We decided to take the Kaibab Trail into the Canyon. Dad said it was really steep but it was the shortest route to the bottom from the South Rim.

We would reach the bottom on the first day, at the Phantom Ranch and we would camp by Bright Angel Creek, not far from the Colorado River. The second day we would begin our climb back up on Bright Angel Trail and camp overnight at Indian Garden Campground, about halfway to the rim. And the third day, we would hike out of the Canyon and arrive at the rim close to El Tovar Lodge.

The hike, camping under the stars, the majesty of the Canyon all seem so wonderful. Although we are entering the Grand Canyon National Park, the Ranger we met last night said the true name should be the Grand Canyon National "Wilderness." This huge slice of mother earth and the physical demands of hiking into her Canyon make this adventure a once in a lifetime journey.

# CHAPTER 2
## First Steps

The sun was barely up and the trail was still in deep shadows when I took my first step into the Canyon. And what a step!

I stretched out my foot – and stretched, and stretched – it seemed like my toe would never touch the ground. Each step on the trail was a lot deeper than I expected, and the landing spot was narrow. I looked back at Drew to make sure he was OK. His eyes were bigger than I'd ever seen, but he was trying to be brave.

I was glad I was ahead of him, so if he stumbled, I could help him. I was glad Dad was in front of me for the same reason!

After about a half an hour of careful steps in the shadows, the sun finally broke onto the trail, filling the Canyon with golden rays that made the Canyon walls change color each minute.

We stopped to look back up at the steep steps we had just come down – I was amazed at how steep it was. Then we turned and looked into the Canyon. The winding, narrow trail hugged the walls and finally disappeared into a gray gloomy shadow way below us. We couldn't see the bottom, so I knew we had a long way to go.

A cautious half hour later spent gauging one adventurous step at a time, the dawn finally broke through the morning chills with a warm orange and yellow glow. We all stopped to look back at the steep trail we had just descended, then turned and looked down into the Canyon to see the winding narrow trail disappear into the gray morning abyss.

"Where are we?" Drew asked.

Dad answered, "We are in the greatest canyon and one of the seven natural wonders of the world."

"Is there a bottom? When will we get there? Are all these steps so big?"

Drew being the youngest had to almost jump down the steps because his legs weren't long enough. He was determined and even though he had questions and the steps were difficult for him, he didn't whine or complain.

I was really proud of him.

I thought about Grandpa Reuben who was in the Army and Grandpa Al who was in the Navy. They both fought in WWII and I never heard them complain once about the War. If anyone was like them, it was Drew. My guess he would be a Marine – and a really good one.

Dad told us that it was a mile to the bottom of the Canyon and depending on how many stops we made to rest, we should be at Phantom Ranch by late afternoon.

"Will we have lunch on the trail?" Drew asked. "What's for lunch? What's for dinner? What's the Phantom Ranch? Sounds scary."

Dad said, "We will have lunch along the trail, and dinner at the Phantom Ranch will all come soon enough."

Then he told a story about our grandpas. Dad was always

doing this – telling family stories to teach us about life. I like it because it made it easier to understand.

"Grandpa Reuben had adult diabetes in his 60's and went on an exercise and diet program to beat it and he did." Dad said. "Then he had heart bypass surgery in his 70s. that would have stopped a lot of men his age, but he was determined to get well, so he did everything the doctors told him to do, and he got well faster than a lot of people much younger than he was. I see a lot of him in you, Drew, and I'm proud of you and how hard you are working on this hike."

That made Drew stand up straighter, and he looked a lot less tired.

Then Dad asked: "What I would like to ask you, Drew, is how old is Grandpa Reuben?"

"He's really old. I don't know, maybe 20?" Drew answered.

Dad and Rick laughed and said Grandpa Reuben was 80.

I wasn't sure what Grandpa Reuben's age had to do with our hike, and then Dad said "While the Canyon is just 6 million years old, the rocks at the top of the Canyon are

270 million years old, and at the bottom, they are 1.8 billion years old.

"To put that in Grandpa years, the Canyon has been around for 75,000 Grandpa lifetimes. The youngest rocks have ben around for more than three thousand million Grandpa lifetimes at the top and more than 22 thousand million Grandpa lifetimes at the bottom."

We love both our grandpas and if there were any grandpas we wish would live 22 thousand million lifetimes, it would be Grandpa Reuben and Grandpa Al. But it was hard to imagine just how big those numbers were. And I wondered why the rocks were older than the Canyon.

# CHAPTER 3
# Kaibab Formation

We once again began our downward descent and no one spoke as we continued to be careful to stay on the narrow trail. The morning sun was climbing in the sky and the full light revealed the steps but we could now see the sheer drop into the vast Canyon on the edge of the trail. The confidence we shared with the first few steps was quickly replaced with fear.

I focused on one careful step after another, never looked up, did not say a word and heard only my own heavy breathing. I was lost in the descent thinking only about not making a misstep when my Dad said, "Let's stop here." I exhaled with relief not knowing that I had been holding my breath with each downward step. Dad said, "Short break. Let's all sit down and take our packs off." We hadn't gone far, but I was really glad to take off my pack, sit on a rock by the trail and rest my trembling legs.

We now had a sense of what Dad and Rick had in mind for us. Stopping every half hour or so to rest and look at the Canyon, which we never would see or appreciate if all we did was concentrate on going down the trail. We took off our packs, had a drink of water and a snack of nuts and dried fruit.

Rick loves to sail and knows all about water, weather and winds. He said, "Water is a powerful source of energy and rapidly moving water can move large rocks and enlarge riverbeds that carve a path through the earth's crust." And then he asked us, "How do you think this huge Canyon was formed?"

Drew said, "Just looks like a big crack in the earth."

"Drew," Rick said, "millions of years ago before there was life on earth, the earth's crust was in motion with all kinds of wind and water moving every which direction creating canyons, plateaus and mesas. All of that activity was in tandem with the changing climate and it was the beginning of the processes that helped to carve and shape the Grand Canyon." He then pointed up to the Kaibab Formation we had just passed. "See the wind blowing against those layers of rocks just under the white layer? The occasional puff of red dust is the wind moving loose particles of the formation and carving the rocks ever so slowly over time."

"Ok," Dad said, "we have just passed the Kaibab and Toroweap formations. Even though this is the youngest rock layer in the Canyon, these formations are 270 million years old. As we continue our hike down into the Canyon, the layers of rocks and formations get older as we travel back in time to when the earth was much older."

"Climate Change? What is that?" I thought to myself. We know we have four seasons with varying degrees of hot and cold, wind, rain and snow. And, I wasn't sure how water or wind or time played a role in forming the Canyon. Something must have happened many years ago to carve this giant canyon of Nature.

14   THE MYSTERY of the GRAND CANYON and CLIMATE CHANGE

# CHAPTER 4
## Ancient Ones

Stepping carefully ever downward, we heard a raven caw then an eerie sound that came from the depths of the Canyon. The raven's screech and the sound from the Canyon passed us like the wind just touching our clothes ever so slightly. We looked into the Canyon and there were rock formations jutting out that looked like human forms. I squinted my eyes to see better and the rocks seemed to move or sway just a little in the wind.

Dad said that the rocks jutting out were lookout points for the Ancient Ones and they used to send alarms from them to the other members of the tribe if someone was coming. Ancient Ones, I thought, now who were they and were they on those rocks warning others of our coming?

Drew misunderstood the word Ancient for Alien and

quickly asked "When did the aliens come to the Canyon and where did they land their spaceships?"

"Drew," said Dad with a chuckle, "there were no aliens in the Canyon. The Ancient Ones were migrating nomads seeking a better life for their families. They are the ones we call Ancient, not Alien."

Dad continued and said "When the Ancient Ones first saw the Canyon, we can imagine they were in awe and must have believed the spirits had led them to this wonderful place. They believed in another world, a place where the spirits lived and only a few people like medicine men and tribe shamans may have visited."

To think that we now answer the call of the Ancient Ones by sensing their presence in the Canyon, their inspiration and beliefs that there is another world and the Grand Canyon may be the entrance to it.

# GRAND CANYON

"You are halfway through the book and I'm sure you are now becoming more curious about the mystery of how the Grand Canyon was formed.

Place yourself in our shoes and walk with us as we continue our hike into the Canyon.

Visualize yourself on the edge of the narrow Kaibab Trail and being almost knocked over by mules bringing mail up the trail from Phantom Ranch.

Look around and see the stunning rock formations that have been carved out of the Canyon over millions of years.

See the red and orange colors of the Canyon walls change from dawn to dusk.

Put your feet into the cold Colorado River water and last of all remember, this is an adventure into a wilderness and we all have a role to play in preserving the mysteries and wonders of nature."

THE MYSTERY of the GRAND CANYON and CLIMATE CHANGE

# CHAPTER 5
# Mules

"Steady everyone," Dad said, "you never know what lies around the next corner." No sooner had Dad warned us again about the narrow path when a caravan of mules came around the corner. "Horses." said Drew. "No" said Dad, "they are mules and stay close to the wall of the path so they can pass."

Drew said "The is no room for them to pass, the trail is too narrow and they will fall off." Just as he said that, they walked passed us one by one so sure footed they never fell. Their feet were just inches from the edge of the trail and they never broke stride or even looked at us when they went by.

We later learned that these are pack mules and some of them take provisions and supplies down to Phantom Ranch and on their return trip, they take out trash and the mail.

Other mules are trained to take tourists in and out of the Canyon. It looked scary to us to be on top of one of those tall mules as they walked so close to the edge.

Amazing to think that every day these hearty animals travel in and out of the Canyon doing their job and, as far as I know, never falling off the trail into the Canyon. (It's only happened a few times in more than one hundred years).

Dad said, "The mules are sure-footed like mountain goats." Drew said "Were the aliens sure footed too?" We all laughed and Dad said the ancients, not the aliens had only game trails to follow and had to be very very careful where they walked because if they became injured, there were no doctors or helicopters to come and rescue them and take care of them. For them, falling into the Canyon or severely hurting themselves meant sure death.

I pictured myself in moccasins climbing down the steep Canyon trails in search of food and water. A very different time long ago when today we wear fancy sneakers and shoes and our only search for food and water is raiding the refrigerator or going to a fast food drive-thru.

It occurred to me that the ancients would consider us aliens if they came into our world and saw how we lived, traveled by airplane and bought our food at a grocery store.

# CHAPTER 6
# Colorado River and Phantom Ranch

After many hours of watching every step we took, we stopped. Dad said "Listen, can you hear that?" We listened and at first all I could hear was our heavy breathing and then I did hear a low roar in the distance.

Rick said "Water. It's the roar of water. I would know that sound anywhere in the world."

We all then listened very carefully and the roar in the distance broke the silence we had fallen into. With the sound of the water, we all got new life as we knew we were near our goal and rest for our weary legs. We pushed on and the roar became louder and louder although we were still a long way from the Colorado River.

Dad said, "We saw the wind moving the dirt and rock in the Kaibab Formation and now you will see the Colorado

River moving rocks and dirt as well as it flows through the Canyon. Between the wind, rain and rushing water, the Canyon was created and is changing every day."

Drew said, "Can we go swimming?" Dad laughed and said "You can but the water is very cold, surprisingly cold when the temperature at the bottom may be over 100 degrees. Besides, the river is too swift and dangerous for casual swimming."

And just like hearing the call of the Ancients, around the next bend we saw the Colorado River for the first time. We finally had arrived at what I thought was the end of the day's hike but we had farther to go to reach Phantom Ranch. All we had to do was to keep on walking and finally reach the campground near the Ranch where we could make camp for the night.

Phantom Ranch is 4,800 feet (just under one mile) below the South Rim and was built in 1922 as a rest stop for Canyon mule riders. Dad said that we had descended through about two billion years of geological history and now here we were at the bottom of the Canyon. This journey to the bottom should always be in our memories as a journey into time.

"What's for dinner, I'm hungry," said Drew. "Ok fine," said Dad, "we will make camp, put our sore and tired feet into Bright Angel Creek and then head to the canteen for dinner. We will have whatever the mules have brought down today for dinner and I'm sure it will be good."

Dad and Rick seemed to be at peace enjoying the end of the first day's hike as they put their feet into the creek running alongside our tents. Dad said, "It's time to reflect on what we have seen and take in the history of the Grand Canyon." Not hearing any response from Drew, I looked over at him and he was sound asleep on his bedroll. Yes, the day had taken its toll on my younger brother.

We had dinner at the Phantom Ranch canteen on long tables with many other hikers who looked as tired as I felt but happy to have a hot meal. After dinner, we walked in the dark back to our tents and fell asleep listening to the Bright Angel Creek next to us and the low roar of the Colorado River in the distance.

# CHAPTER 7
## Indian Garden

Up at dawn, we had breakfast over a campfire, rolled up our tents and began the next leg of our journey up Bright Angel Trail.

Our destination today was Indian Garden where there were restrooms and a campsite for us to stay overnight.

The trail that would take us to the rim was the Bright Angel Trail and although longer than the Kaibab Trail, it was not as steep with as many switchbacks. We planned a half-day trip to Indian Garden before we took on the last part of the trail to the rim on the third day. This was a good plan; however, little did we realize we would now be using a whole different set of leg muscles and breathing would become more difficult as we climbed up and out of the Canyon.

We noticed more people on this trail since it was wider and

easier to walk on than the Kaibab Trail. Some people were running down the trail and we wondered if they would be really sore when they reached the bottom. Hikers heading up the trail weren't running and looked more like us—tired and just concentrating on putting one foot in front of the other.

We stopped and rested many times and Dad filled us in on the different rock formations and the many animals who make their home in the Canyon.

Dad said, "The very first inhabitants of the Canyon were sea creatures and we can find their fossil remains in different parts of the Canyon. Where they lived was once a sea and they were very small and date back about 500 million years."

"Did dinosaurs hike into the Canyon?" Drew asked." We all laughed. "No Drew," I said. "I don't think a brontosaurus traveled down the Kaibab Trail with a backpack and a baseball cap." "In fact," said Dad, "dinosaurs didn't evolve until about 40 million years after the Canyon's youngest layer was formed. The first animals to live in the Canyon, other than the sea creatures found in the ocean floor, were things like giant ground sloths and an extinct species of mountain goat."

"Today there are Bighorn sheep, ravens, hawks, peregrine falcons and a large bird called the California Condor. California Condors date to the last Ice Age and almost became extinct until some were rescued by humans and raised in captivity. They were well taken care of and soon their numbers increased to a point where they could be reintroduced into the Canyon. They are the largest land-based bird on the continent and have a 10-foot wingspan. They are here but are closer to the area called Vermillion Cliffs where the Colorado first enters into the Canyon north and east of here. They like that area because it has many remote areas where they can roost and have little condors."

I was just as glad they were far away. I didn't want to think what it would be like if one of those giant birds swooped down on us.

Finally, we saw Indian Garden. It was time to rest and look for fossils and condors.

# CHAPTER 8
## The Rim

Before we left Indian Garden, I saw Dad was doing something to his bare toes. It turned out that he not only didn't get in shape for the hike and was having breathing problems, he also made the mistake of wearing an old pair of very hard leather boots. Although we had stopped a lot going down the Kaibab Trail, every time Dad took a step his toes got squished into the hard toe of his boot and he got blisters under his toenails. He said that he was going to have to relieve the pressure under his toenails so he could continue on without pain. I didn't want to watch but what I saw him do was to take a hot needle and punch a hole into each of his ten toenails which then relieved the pressure by allowing the blood to ooze out the pin-hole. Yuck. Not pretty but he got it done, wrapped his toes in bandages and was ready for the climb out. Phew, surgery at Indian Garden.

We began the final leg to hike out of the Canyon and stopped many times for Dad to catch his breath and rest his toes. This gave us time to take in the beauty of the Canyon, look at the different layers of rock and keep our eyes out for condors.

The Colorado River was now far below us and out of sight. All we could think of was pressing on to continue climbing ever upward, to finally reach the Rim and level ground!

Rick was in better shape than my Dad and he carried Dad's backpack the last quarter mile to make the climb easier on him. Rick was a great guy, continuing to encourage my Dad to rest and drink water and take his time. I think Rick was afraid my Dad was going to have a heart attack and die right there on the Bright Angel Trail.

Ryan and I ran ahead of everyone, wanting to be the first ones out of the Canyon. It seemed like a good idea at the time; however, when we finally made it to the Rim and level ground, we both collapsed with exhaustion.

We did it! We made it to the top! About a half hour later, Dad, with Drew and Rick behind him, came huffing and puffing up the trail and I could see they were tired but really happy to finally reach the Rim.

Yes, an adventure of a lifetime and memories to never forget.

We had some people standing by the Rim take pictures of us and to this day, those photos look like we had just crossed the Sahara Desert — dusty, tired and sweaty.

Dad said, once he caught his breath, "We all deserve a Survivor T-shirt, we made it!"

Smiles all round.

# Reflections

My Dad is a dreamer and as we stood at the rim and looked back into the Canyon, he said, "The Grand Canyon is an awesome example of the history of the Earth. The forces of Nature carved this masterpiece for us to see and give us pause to reflect."

You now know that the earth is in motion, contracting and expanding every day as it circles the sun."

Dad paused, then continued, "The evolving Earth's core coupled with climate change is as real as the air we breathe and the water we drink."

Drew piped up, "Climate change Dad? That's new to me but I think I understand. It's complicated but unless we take care of our planet, we could become the next generation of dinosaurs."

"Well said, little brother, well said."

CPSIA information can be obtained
at www.ICGtesting.com
Printed in the USA
BVHW062034030622
638689BV00001B/6